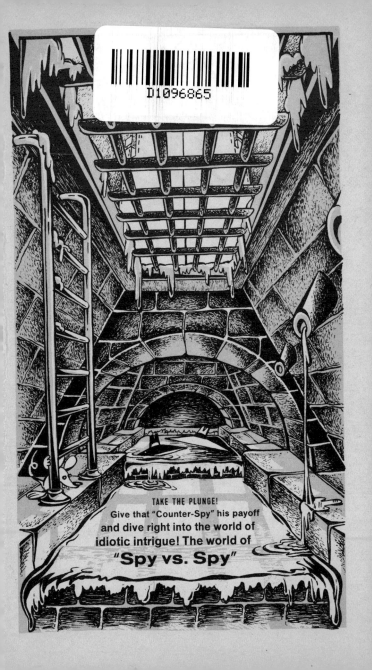

TAKE THE PLUNGE!
Give that "Counter-Spy" his payoff
and dive right into the world of
idiotic intrigue! The world of
"Spy vs. Spy"

FOLLOW-UP FILE

by

ANTONIO PROHIAS

Edited by

ALBERT B. FELDSTEIN

WARNER PAPERBACK LIBRARY EDITION

First Printing: May, 1975

Copyright © 1968, 1975 by Antonio Prohias
and E.C. Publications, Inc.

Warner Paperback Library is a division of Warner Books, Inc., 75 Rockefeller Plaza, New York, N.Y. 10019.

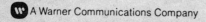 A Warner Communications Company

Printed in the United States of America

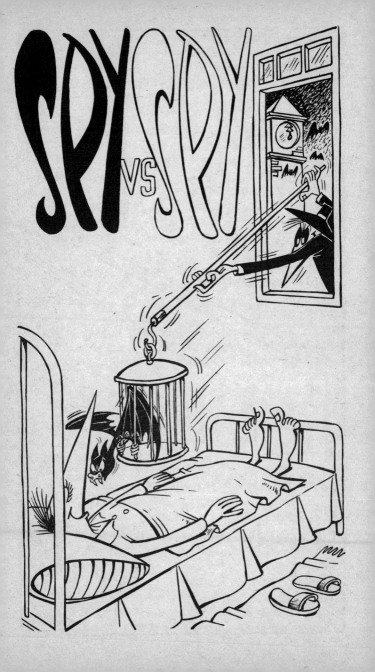

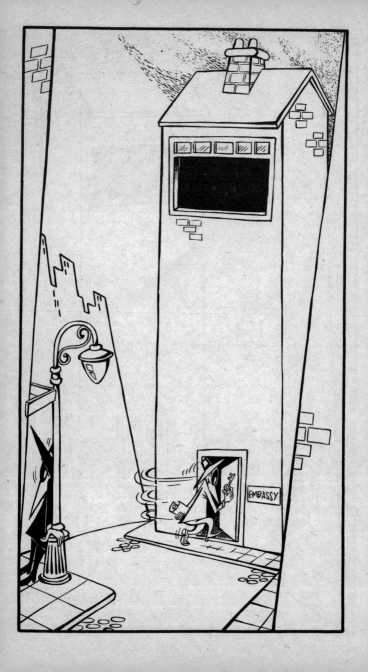

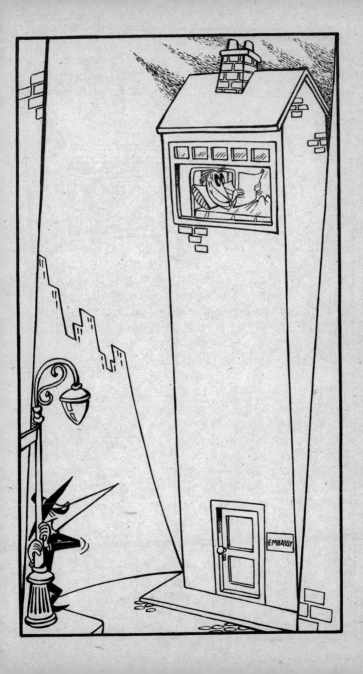

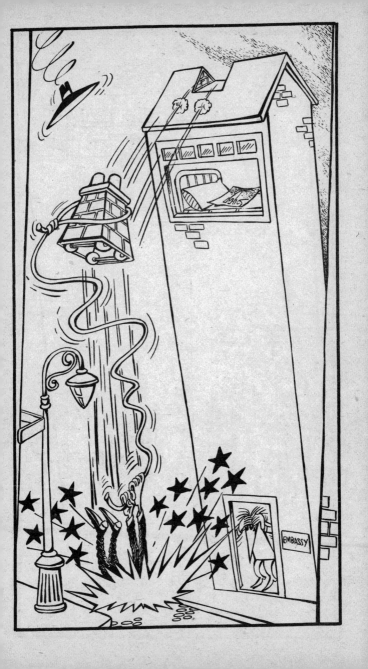

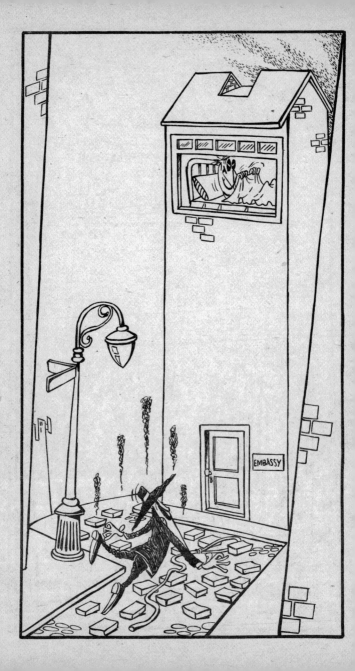

EMBASSY

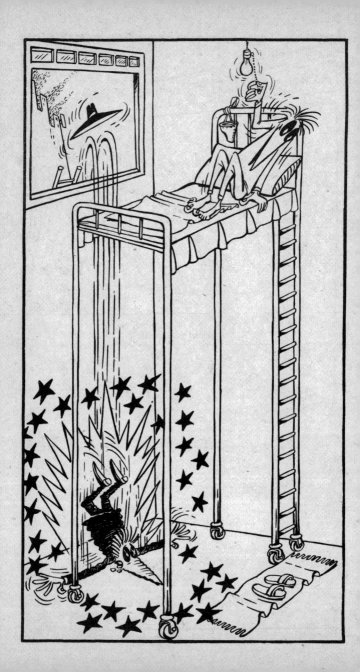

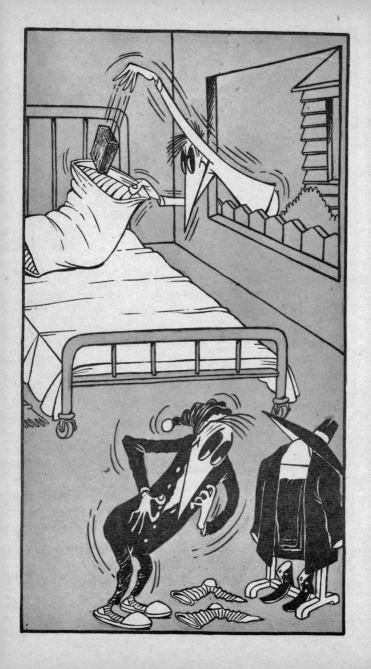

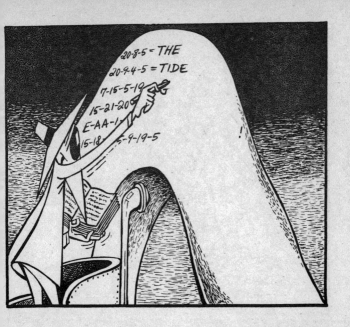

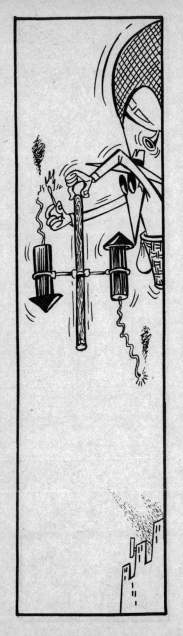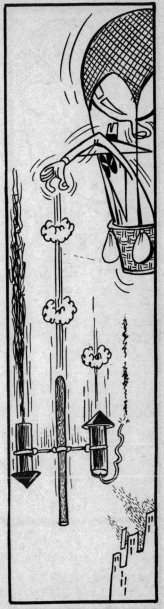

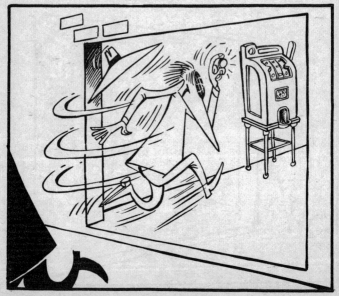

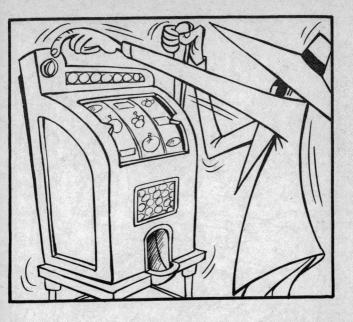

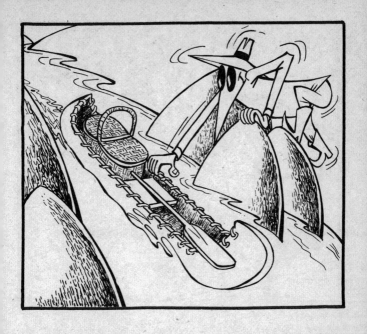

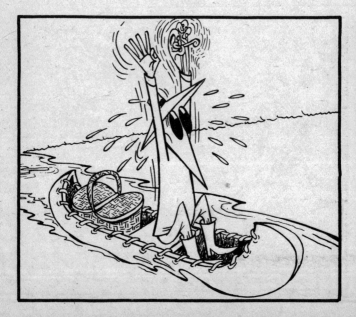

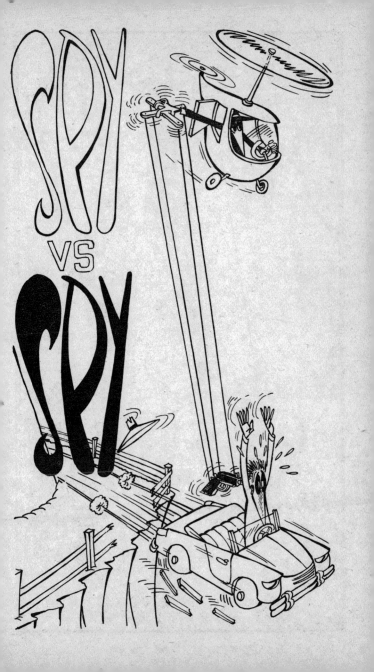

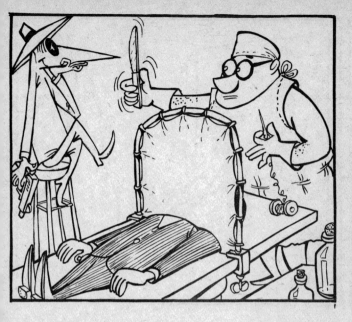

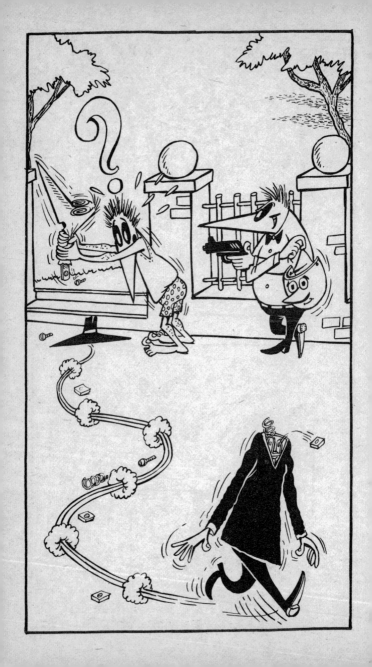

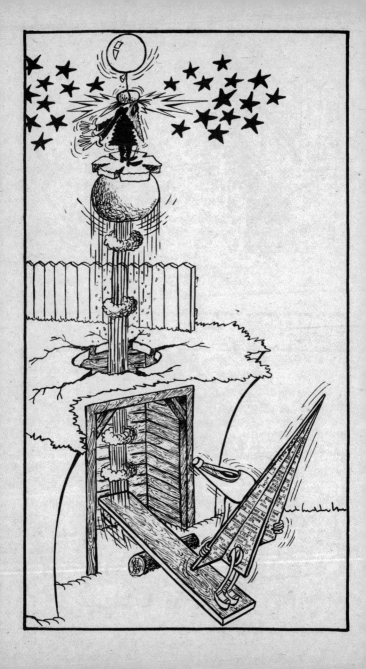

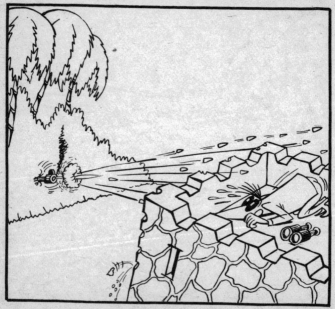

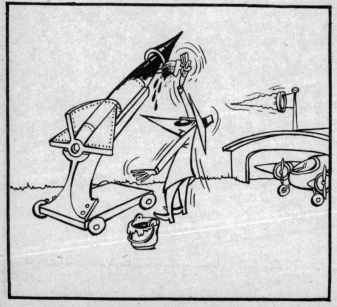

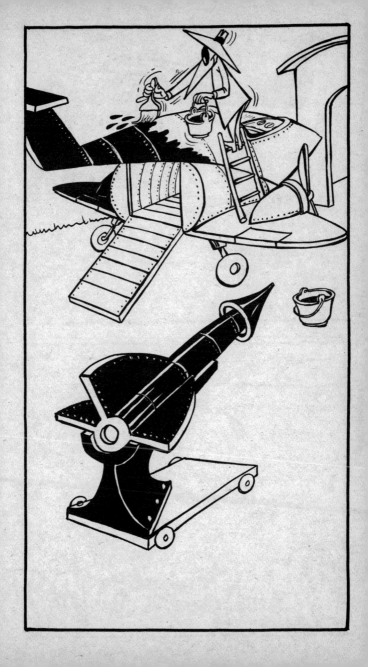

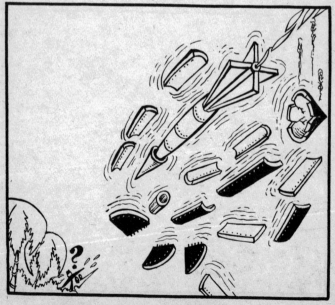

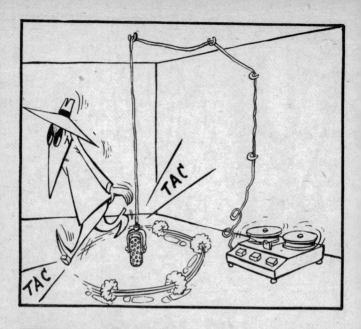

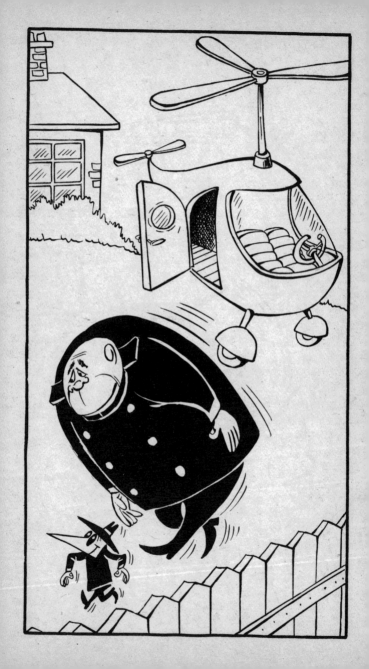

MAIL COLLECTION
11.00 P.M.

TICK
TICK

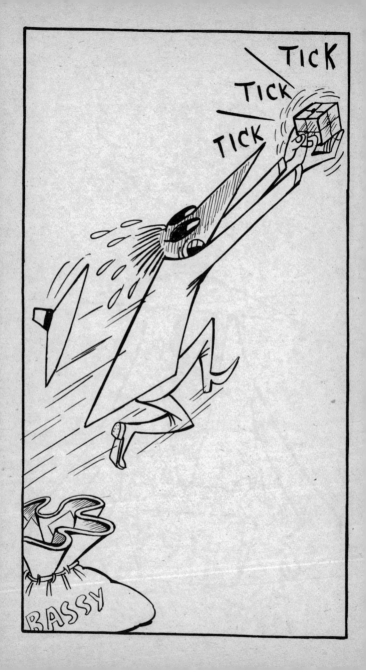